RHYMES
for
BEDTIME

Contents

Material in this edition was previously published by Ladybird Books in the *Nursery Rhymes* gift book.

Published by Ladybird Books Ltd.
27 Wrights Lane London W8 5TZ
A Penguin Company
10 9 8 7 6 5 4 3 2

Ladybird

RHYMES *for* BEDTIME

Chosen by RONNE RANDALL
Illustrated by PETER STEVENSON

The Evening Is Coming

The evening is coming, the sun sinks to rest,
The birds are all flying straight home to the nest.
"Caw," says the crow as he flies overhead,
"It's time little children were going to bed!"

The butterfly, drowsy, has folded its wing.
The bees are returning, no more the birds sing.
Their labour is over, their nestlings are fed.
It's time little children were going to bed.

Here comes the pony, his work is all done,
Down through the meadow he takes a good run.
Up go his heels and down goes his head.
It's time little children were going to bed.

Now the Day Is Over

Now the day is over,
Night is drawing nigh.
Shadows of the evening
Steal across the sky.

Down with the Lambs

Down with the lambs,
    Up with the lark,
Run to bed, children,
    Before it gets dark.

Goosey, Goosey, Gander

Goosey, goosey, gander,
    Whither shall I wander?
Upstairs, downstairs,
    In my lady's chamber.
There I met an old man
    Who would not say his prayers.
I took him by the left leg
    And threw him down the stairs.

Jack and Jill

Jack and Jill went up the hill
To fetch a pail of water.
Jack fell down and broke his crown,
And Jill came tumbling after.

Up Jack got, and home did trot,
As fast as he could caper,
To old Dame Dob, who patched his head
With vinegar and brown paper.

Mary Had a Little Lamb

Mary had a little lamb,
Its fleece was white as snow,
And everywhere that Mary went
The lamb was sure to go.

It followed her to school one day,
Which was against the rule.
It made the children laugh and play
To see a lamb at school.

And so the teacher turned it out,
But still it lingered near,
And waited patiently about
Till Mary did appear.

"What makes the lamb love Mary so?"
The eager children cry.
"Why, Mary loves the lamb, you know,"
The teacher did reply.

Mary at the Kitchen Door

One, two, three, four,
Mary at the kitchen door.
Five, six, seven, eight,
Eating cherries off a plate.

One's None

One's none,
Two's some,
Three's many,
Four's a penny,
Five's a little hundred.

Three Little Ghostesses

Three little ghostesses,
Sitting on postesses,
Eating buttered toastesses,
Greasing up their fistesses,
Up to their wristesses.
Oh, what beastesses,
To make such feastesses!

One, Two, Three

One, two, three,
I love coffee,
And Billy loves tea.
How good you be,
One, two, three,
I love coffee,
And Billy loves tea.

There Were Three Cooks

There were three cooks of Colebrook,
And they fell out with our cook.
And all was for the pudding he took
From the three cooks of Colebrook.

Twinkle, Twinkle

Twinkle, twinkle, little star,
How I wonder what you are!
Up above the world so high,
Like a diamond in the sky.

When the blazing sun is gone,
When he nothing shines upon,
Then you show your little light,
Twinkle, twinkle, all the night.

In the dark blue sky you keep,
And often through my curtains peep,
For you never shut your eye,
Till the sun is in the sky.

Jane Taylor

Star Light

Star light, star bright,
First star I see tonight,
I wish I may, I wish I might,
Have the wish I wish tonight.

I See the Moon

I see the moon,
And the moon sees me.
God bless the moon,
And God bless me.

The Man in the Moon

The Man in the Moon looked out of the moon,
    And this is what he said:
"Now that I'm getting up, 'tis time
    All children went to bed!"

Wee Willie Winkie

Wee Willie Winkie runs through the town,
Upstairs and downstairs in his nightgown,
Rapping at the window, crying through the lock,
"Are the children all in bed, for now it's eight o'clock!"

Come, Let's to Bed

"Come, let's to bed,"
Says Sleepy-head.
"Tarry awhile," says Slow.
"Put on the pan,"
Says Greedy Nan,
"Let's sup before we go."

A Glass of Milk

A glass of milk and a slice of bread,
And then good night, we must go to bed.

Sippity Sup

Sippity sup, sippity sup,
Bread and milk from a china cup.
Bread and milk from a bright silver spoon,
Made of a piece of the bright silver moon!
Sippity sup, sippity sup,
Sippity, sippity sup!

Go to Bed First

Go to bed first, a golden purse;
Go to bed second, a golden pheasant;
Go to bed third, a golden bird.

Go to Bed Late

Go to bed late,
Stay very small.
Go to bed early,
Grow very tall.

The Sandman

The Sandman comes,
The Sandman comes.
He has such pretty snow-white sand,
And well he's known throughout the land.
The Sandman comes.

All the Pretty Little Horses

Hush-a-bye, don't you cry,
Go to sleep little baby.
When you wake, you shall have
All the pretty little horses.
Blacks and bays, dapples and greys,
Coach and six little horses.

Bossy-Cow, Bossy-Cow

Bossy-cow, bossy-cow, where do you lie?
In the green meadows, under the sky.

Billy-horse, billy-horse, where do you lie?
Out in the stable, with nobody nigh.

Birdies bright, birdies sweet, where do you lie?
Up in the treetops, ever so high.

Baby dear, baby love, where do you lie?
In my warm cradle, with Mama close by.

Hush, Little Baby

Hush, little baby, don't say a word,

Papa's going to buy you a mockingbird.

If that mockingbird won't sing,

Papa's going to buy you a diamond ring.

If that diamond ring turns brass,

Papa's going to buy you a looking glass.

If that looking glass gets broke,

Papa's going to buy you a billy goat.

If that billy goat won't pull,

Papa's going to buy you a cart and bull.

If that cart and bull turn over,

Papa's going to buy you a dog named Rover.

If that dog named Rover won't bark,

Papa's going to buy you a horse and cart.

If that horse and cart fall down,

You'll still be the sweetest little baby in town.

Hush-a-bye, Baby

Hush-a-bye, baby, lie still in the cradle,
Mother has gone to buy a soup ladle.
When she comes back, she'll bring us some meat,
And Father and baby shall have some to eat.

Dear Baby, Lie Still

Hush-a-bye, baby, lie still with thy daddy,
Thy mammy has gone to the mill,
To get some meal, to make a cake,
So pray, my dear baby, lie still.

Rock-a-bye, Baby, Rock

Rock-a-bye, baby, rock, rock, rock,
Baby shall have a new pink frock!
A new pink frock and a ribbon to tie,
If baby is good and does not cry.

Rock-a-bye, baby, rock, rock, rock,
Listen, who comes with a knock, knock, knock?
Oh, it is pussy! Come in, come in!
Mother and baby are always at home.

Raisins and Almonds

To my baby's cradle in the night
Comes a little goat all snowy-white.
The goat will trot to the market,
While Mother her watch does keep,
Bringing back raisins and almonds.
Sleep, my little one, sleep.

Hush-a-bye, Baby, on the Treetop

Hush-a-bye, baby, on the treetop,
When the wind blows, the cradle will rock.
When the bough breaks, the cradle will fall,
And down will come baby, cradle and all.

Sleep, Baby, Sleep

Sleep, baby, sleep,
Thy father guards the sheep,
Thy mother shakes the dreamland tree,
And from it fall sweet dreams for thee.
Sleep, baby, sleep.

Sleep, baby, sleep,
Our cottage vale is deep.
The little lamb is on the green,
With woolly fleece so soft and clean.
Sleep, baby, sleep.

Sleep, baby, sleep,
Down where the woodbines creep.
Be always like the lamb so mild,
A kind and sweet and gentle child.
Sleep, baby, sleep.

Cradle Song

Lullaby and good night, with roses bedight,
With lilies bedecked is baby's wee bed.
Lay thee down now and rest,
May thy slumber be blessed.
Lay thee down now and rest,
May thy slumber be blessed.

Lullaby and good night, thy mother's delight,
Bright angels around my darling shall stand.
They will guard thee from harms,
Thou shalt wake in my arms.
They will guard thee from harms,
Thou shalt wake in my arms.

Johannes Brahms

Jack Sprat

Jack Sprat could eat no fat,
His wife could eat no lean,
And so between them both,
They licked the platter clean.

Jack ate all the lean,
Joan ate all the fat.
The bone they picked clean,
Then gave it to the cat.

Old Mother Hubbard

Old Mother Hubbard
Went to the cupboard
To fetch her poor dog a bone.
But when she got there
The cupboard was bare,
And so the poor dog had none.

There Was an Old Woman

There was an old woman tossed up in a blanket,
    Seventeen times as high as the moon.
But where she was going no mortal could tell,
    For under her arm she carried a broom.
"Old woman, old woman, old woman," said I,
    "Whither, oh whither, oh whither so high?"
"To sweep the cobwebs from the sky,
    And I'll be with you by and by!"

Hey, Diddle, Diddle

Hey, diddle, diddle,
The cat and the fiddle,
The cow jumped over the moon.
The little dog laughed
To see such sport,
And the dish ran away with the spoon!

The Man in the Moon
Came Tumbling Down

The man in the moon came tumbling down,
And asked the way to Norwich.
He went by south, and burnt his mouth
With supping cold pease porridge.

Pease Porridge Hot

Pease porridge hot,
Pease porridge cold,
Pease porridge in the pot,
Nine days old.

Some like it hot,
Some like it cold,
Some like it in the pot,
Nine days old.

One Misty, Moisty Morning

One misty, moisty morning,
When cloudy was the weather,
I met with an old man
Clothed all in leather,
Clothed all in leather,
With cap under his chin.
"How do you?" and "How do you do?"
And "How do you do?" again.

Doctor Foster

Doctor Foster went to Gloucester
    In a shower of rain.
He stepped in a puddle, right up to his middle,
    And never went there again.

The Old Woman Who Lived in a Shoe

There was an old woman who lived in a shoe,
She had so many children she didn't know what to do.
She gave them some broth without any bread,
Then scolded them soundly and sent them to bed.

Peter, Peter, Pumpkin Eater

Peter, Peter, pumpkin eater,
Had a wife and couldn't keep her.
He put her in a pumpkin shell,
And there he kept her very well.

Peter, Peter, pumpkin eater,
Had another, and didn't love her.
Peter learned to read and spell,
And then he loved her very well.

Georgie Porgie

Georgie Porgie, pudding and pie,
Kissed the girls and made them cry.
When the boys came out to play,
Georgie Porgie ran away.

Tweedledum and Tweedledee

Tweedledum and Tweedledee
    Agreed to fight a battle,
For Tweedledum said Tweedledee
    Had spoilt his nice new rattle.
Just then flew by a monstrous crow
    As big as a tar barrel,
Which frightened both the heroes so,
    They quite forgot their quarrel.

Up the Wooden Hill

Up the wooden hill
     To Bedfordshire,
Down Sheet Lane
     To Blanket Fair.

Diddle, Diddle, Dumpling

Diddle, diddle, dumpling, my son John
Went to bed with his trousers on.
One shoe off, and one shoe on,
Diddle, diddle, dumpling, my son John.

Babyland

How many miles to Babyland?
Anyone can tell.
Up one flight, to your right,
Please to ring the bell.

What do they do in Babyland?
Dream and wake and play,
Laugh and crow, fonder grow,
Jolly times have they.

Rock-a-bye Baby

Rock-a-bye baby, thy cradle is green,
Father's a nobleman, Mother's a queen.
Betty's a lady and wears a gold ring,
And Johnny's a drummer, and drums for the King.

Twelve Huntsmen

Twelve huntsmen with horns and hounds,
Hunting over other men's grounds.

Eleven ships sailing o'er the main,
Some bound for France and some for Spain,
I wish them all safe home again.

Ten comets in the sky,
Some low and some high.

Nine peacocks in the air,
I wonder how they all came there?
I do not know, and I do not care.

Eight joiners in Joiners' Hall,
Working with their tools and all.

Seven lobsters in a dish,
As fresh as any heart could wish.

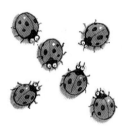

Six beetles against the wall,
Close by an old woman's apple stall.

Five puppies of our dog Ball,
Who daily for their breakfast call.

Four horses stuck in a bog,
Three monkeys tied to a clog.

Two pudding-ends would choke a dog,

With a gaping, wide-mouthed, waddling frog.

One, Two, Three, Four, Five

One, two, three, four, five,
Once I caught a fish alive.
Why did you let it go?
Because it bit my finger so.

Six, seven, eight, nine, ten,
Shall we go to fish again?
Not today, some other time,
For I have broke my fishing line.

Three Wise Men

Three wise men of Gotham
Went to sea in a bowl.
If the bowl had been stronger,
My song would be longer!

I Saw Three Ships

I saw three ships come sailing by,
    Come sailing by, come sailing by.
I saw three ships come sailing by,
    On New Year's Day in the morning!

And what do you think was in them then,
    Was in them then, was in them then?
And what do you think was in them then,
    On New Year's Day in the morning?

Three pretty girls were in them then,
    Were in them then, were in them then.
Three pretty girls were in them then,
    On New Year's Day in the morning.

One could whistle and one could sing,
    And one could play the violin.
Such joy there was at my wedding,
    On New Year's Day in the morning!

Hickory, Dickory, Dock

Hickory, dickory, dock,
The mouse ran up the clock.
The clock struck one,
The mouse ran down.
Hickory, dickory, dock!

Pussy Cat, Pussy Cat

Pussy cat, pussy cat, where have you been?
"I've been to London to visit the Queen."
Pussy cat, pussy cat, what did you there?
"I frightened a little mouse under the chair."

Six Little Mice

Six little mice sat down to spin,
Pussy passed by, and she peeped in.
What are you doing, my little men?
"We're weaving shirts for gentlemen."
Can I come in and cut off your threads?
"No, no, Mistress Pussy, you'd cut off our heads!"

I Love Little Pussy

I love little pussy, her coat is so warm,
And if I don't hurt her, she'll do me no harm.
So I'll not pull her tail, nor drive her away,
But pussy and I very gently will play.

Baa, Baa, Black Sheep

Baa, baa, black sheep, have you any wool?
Yes, sir, yes, sir, three bags full.
One for the master, and one for the dame,
And one for the little boy who lives in the lane.

Little Boy Blue

Little Boy Blue, come blow your horn!
The sheep's in the meadow, the cow's in the corn.
Where is the boy who looks after the sheep?
He's under the haycock, fast asleep.
Will you wake him? No, not I!
For if I do, he's sure to cry.

Little Bo-peep

Little Bo-peep has lost her sheep,
And doesn't know where to find them.
Leave them alone, and they'll come home,
Bringing their tails behind them.

Little Bo-peep fell fast asleep,
And dreamt she heard them bleating.
But when she awoke, she found it a joke,
For they were still a-fleeting.

Then up she took her little crook,
Determined for to find them.
She found them indeed, but it made her heart bleed,
For they'd left their tails behind them.

Come to the Window

Come to the window,
My baby, with me,
And look at the stars
That shine on the sea!
There are two little stars
That play at bo-peep
With two little fishes
Far down in the deep,
And two little frogs
Cry, "Neap, neap, neap,
I see a dear baby
That should be asleep!"

Sweet and Low

Sweet and low, sweet and low,
    Wind of the western sea.
Low, low, breathe and blow,
    Wind of the western sea!
Over the rolling waters go,
Come from the dying moon, and blow,
    Blow him again to me;
While my little one, while my pretty one, sleeps.

Sleep and rest, sleep and rest,
    Father will come to thee soon;
Rest, rest, on mother's breast,
    Father will come to thee soon.
Father will come to his babe in the nest,
Silver sails all out of the west,
    Under the silver moon;
Sleep, my little one, sleep, my pretty one, sleep.

Alfred, Lord Tennyson

French Cradle Song

If my boy sleep quietly,
He shall see the busy bee,
When it has made its honey fine,
Dancing in the bright sunshine.

If my boy will slumber,
Angels without number
Will draw near, so fair and bright,
For they only come at night.

Sleep, Oh Sleep

Sleep, oh sleep,
While breezes so softly are blowing.
Sleep, oh sleep,
While streamlets so gently are flowing.
Sleep, oh sleep!

Sleep, oh sleep,
While birds in the forest are singing.
Sleep, oh sleep,
While echoes with music are ringing.
Sleep, oh sleep!

Sleep, oh sleep,
While angels are watching beside thee.
Sleep, oh sleep,
May blessings for ever betide thee.
Sleep, oh sleep.

Quiet the Night

Quiet the night,
Soft is the breeze.
Dim is the light
Of the faraway moon.

Sleep, children, sleep,
Be not alarmed,
Angels on guard
Will keep you unharmed.

Golden Slumbers

Golden slumbers kiss your eyes,
Smiles awake you when you rise.
Sleep, pretty baby, do not cry,
And I will sing you a lullaby.
Rock them, rock them, lullaby.

Good Night

Good night,
Sleep tight,
Wake up bright
In the morning light
To do what's right
With all your might.